SWEET PETE
What do you eat?

Written by Jody Chesko
Illustrations by Diana K. Mathena

RPSS - Rock Paper Safety Scissors Publishing

Rock, Paper, Safety Scissors, 429 Englewood Avenue, Kenmore, NY 14223
publisher@rockpapersafetyscissors.com

978-1-956688-06-1   Sweet Pete What Do You Eat - Hardcover
Printed in the USA

RPSS - Rock Paper Safety Scissors Publishing

**Recommended for children ages 4-8,
and adults hopeful of our future**

For my parents
Richard and Ruth,
for giving me wings to fly.

Hi, I'm Hank, and this is Pete. Have you ever wondered what animals eat?

A lot of them are in our yard,
and I have two at home.

My inside pets like to snuggle.
The animals outside can roam.

My friend, the robin,
gives each baby a turn.

Their beaks are wide open
for a tasty little worm.

My pal, the squirrel,
climbs very tall trees.

She loves to eat nuts
while enjoying the breeze.

I spot a furry bunny
crunching on the tall grass.

She only looks up
to see a bird pass.

My buddy, the horse,
wags his tail all day.

When he gets hungry,
he nibbles on hay.

My best friend is Daisy.
She lives right next door.

Finding bugs with her is fun.
We love to explore!

My dog's name is Pete.
He barks when he's hungry.

His crunching sounds loud.
The kibble is yummy.

My cat's name is Fluffy.
Her fur feels like silk.

She gets a treat today.
I serve her warm milk.

Pete's been a good dog.
I'll throw him a bone.

What kind of foods do you like?
Do you have pets in your home?

Eat well.
Eat Healthy!

Author:

Jody Chesko is a mother, wife, and business owner. You hold in your hands her lifelong dream.

Enjoy!

Ilustrator:

Diana K. Mathena is an artist and designer who has been creating colorful paintings and imaginative spaces for many years.

Sweet Pete is her first children's book.

CPSIA information can be obtained
at www.ICGtesting.com
Printed in the USA
BVHW021736221121
622232BV00004B/71